Boost Creative Writing

Planning Sheets to Support Writers (Especially SEN Pupils) in Years 5–6

Judith Thornby

Brilliant
PUBLICATIONS

We hope you and your pupils enjoy using the ideas in this book. Brilliant Publications publishes many other books to help primary school teachers. To find out more details on all of our titles, including those listed below, please log onto our website: www.brilliantpublications.co.uk.

Boost Creative Writing – Years 1–2	978-1-78317-058-6
Boost Creative Writing – Years 3–4	978-1-78317-059-3
Brilliant Activities for Reading Comprehension, Year 1	978-1-78317-070-8
Brilliant Activities for Reading Comprehension, Year 2	978-1-78317-071-5
Brilliant Activities for Reading Comprehension, Year 3	978-1-78317-072-2
Brilliant Activities for Reading Comprehension, Year 4	978-1-78317-073-9
Brilliant Activities for Reading Comprehension, Year 5	978-1-78317-074-6
Brilliant Activities for Reading Comprehension, Year 6	978-1-78317-075-3
Brilliant Activities for Creative Writing, Year 1	978-0-85747-463-6
Brilliant Activities for Creative Writing, Year 2	978-0-85747-464-3
Brilliant Activities for Creative Writing, Year 3	978-0-85747-465-0
Brilliant Activities for Creative Writing, Year 4	978-0-85747-466-7
Brilliant Activities for Creative Writing, Year 5	978-0-85747-467-4
Brilliant Activities for Creative Writing, Year 6	978-0-85747-468-1

Published by Brilliant Publications
Unit 10
Sparrow Hall Farm
Edlesborough
Dunstable
Bedfordshire
LU6 2ES, UK

www.brilliantpublications.co.uk

The name Brilliant Publications and the logo are registered trademarks.

Written by Judith Thornby
Illustrated by Chantal Kees
Cover illustration by Frank Endersby
Designed by Brilliant Publications

© Text Judith Thornby 2014
© Design Brilliant Publications 2014

Printed book ISBN: 978-1-78317-060-9
E-book ISBN: 978-1-78317-063-0

First printed and published in the UK in 2014

The right of Judith Thornby to be identified as the author of this work has been asserted by herself in accordance with the Copyright, Designs and Patents Act 1988.

Contents

Introduction

These series of planning sheets aim to provide a structured resource which gives plenty of scope for exploring and collecting ideas in the different writing genres: adventure, fantasy, recount, letter, poetry etc. They generate discussion within a defined framework and then aid pupils to write more descriptive stories and compose longer pieces of writing.

Reluctant writers or those writers who struggle with the organization of their ideas can express themselves with more self-assurance by using these planning sheets. Confident writers can also benefit by delving into them to gain further ideas.

Some sheets can be written on directly but many are designed as a prop to refer to when writing. Vocabulary sheets are incorporated with some stories to help the flow of ideas.

Story mountain and mind map templates are included to assist narrative and descriptive writing and to cater for different learning styles. Visual learners have lots of imaginative ideas but might struggle with the sequence of events or the bare skeleton of the story so can benefit from using the story mountain approach. Logical systematic learners can sequence ideas but might struggle to develop them creatively and can benefit from using the mind map templates to expand descriptive writing.

I have specialized in the field of learning support since 1997 when I gained a diploma in specific learning difficulties. I am especially interested in promoting creative writing skills with children who are reluctant writers or who struggle with the organization of their ideas. These series of planning sheets generate discussion and aid in structuring composition in the different writing genres. They also can be used to give further ideas to confident writers as well. I have found that they have been successful in giving pupils greater self-assurance to express themselves in written form and have helped to make writing an enjoyable experience!

On page 5 you will see how the activities in the book link to the 2014 National Curriculum for England. On page 6 there are suggested writing targets. The way I use these is to cut out the relevant one(s) and tape them to the top of the sheets prior to copying, so that pupils have the targets in front of them as they work. These can be used in conjunction with the Editing checklists on pages 7–9.

On pages 10–19 there is a little booklet: 'It's Fun to Write Tip Sheets'. These can be printed and bound to make a useful reference booklet for pupils, or sheets can be given individually to pupils as and when required.

Links to the National Curriculum

The sheets in **Boost Creative Writing** will help Year 5 and 6 pupils to develop their composition skills, as set out in the National Curriculum for England (2014).

Composition

The sheets in **Boost Creative Writing** help pupils to plan their writing, by providing a structured format for discussing and recording their ideas. The sheets provide pupils with the opportunity to write for a variety of different genre and audiences. Some sample pieces of writing are given, but pupils would benefit from discussing and analysing the structure, vocabulary and grammar used in other similar texts. When writing narratives pupils are encouraged to look at the development of characters and settings.

All pupils, but especially SEN pupils, will find it very beneficial to have the opportunity to talk about what they are going to write prior to doing so, as often pupils' writing ability lags behind their speaking ability. Composing and rehearsing sentences orally, prior to writing, helps them to build a varied and rich vocabulary and encourages an increased range of sentence structures.

The sheets in this book can be used to help children to become aware of, and start to use, features of writing. In narratives, the structured format of the sheets encourages them to think and talk about the setting, characters and plot. Similarly, for non-narrative pieces, the way the sheets are formatted encourages pupils to think about how they will structure their writing.

When pupils have finished their writing, they should be encouraged to re-read their work and to think about how it can be improved. The editing checklists on pages 7–9 and the It's Fun to Write Tip Sheets on pages 10–19 will help with this. Discussing their work with you and with other pupils will help them to assess the effectiveness of their own writing.

Reading their writing aloud helps children to see that their writing is valued. Encourage pupils to use appropriate intonation and to control the tone and volume so that the meaning is clear.

Vocabulary, grammar and punctuation

Many of the sheets contain suggested vocabulary to encourage children to extend their range of vocabulary and prompt them to use new words in their writing. The activities can also be used to reinforce children's understanding of grammar and punctuation, but this is not the primary purpose of the sheets.

Suggested writing targets

To have an opening, middle and ending in my writing
To understand how to use paragraphs in my writing
To understanding the story mountain structure of narrative writing: opening, build up, climax, resolution, ending
To discuss and plan my story before writing using a story mountain or mind map
To use interesting verbs when writing the build-up part of the story
To use powerful adjectives in a description
To describe a character in detail
To describe a setting in detail
To use a range of adjectives, powerful verbs and adverbs to make the description sparkle
To understand the main ways authors use to start a story: setting, character, speech, statement or a question
To write 3 story starters using the different ways authors employ
To write an interesting opening paragraph with a hook to keep the reader interested
To check that I am writing in the same tense
To read over my writing, checking that I have put in capital letters and full stops
To use time connectives to start my sentences in different ways: Then… Suddenly… Next minute… Meanwhile… Eventually…
To use speech marks correctly and start a new line when someone is speaking
To use a repeating line in a poem
To plan and write an information booklet
To recount real events in the order they happened
To write a descriptive poem using personification or simile to paint an image in words
To use sensory description in my writing – What can you see? hear? smell? taste? How are you feeling?
To use connectives to elongate my sentences
To establish a different viewpoint in writing
To present different sides of a viewpoint
To use techniques to create suspense or excitement, such as varying sentence length or asking a question
To take time reading over my work: check for punctuation, grammar, spelling errors or omitted words needed for meaning
To create interesting opening lines to really grip the reader's interest

Boost Creative Writing, Years 5–6
© Judith Thornby and Brilliant Publications

Editing checklist – narrative writing

	✓	
Clear structure of plot Introduction, middle, ending Story mountain structure		
Paragraphs 4+		
Interesting vocabulary Replace over-used words		
Build up description – adjectives Imagery: simile, metaphor, personification. What do you see? hear? smell? taste? feel?		
Create suspense Paragraph hook		
Vary sentence length Short sentences for suspense and action. Longer sentences for description.		
Use connectives Next… After a while… Meanwhile… etc		
Reader understanding Have you written what you meant to say?		
Speech New line for each new speaker		
Tense – past or present? Keep in the same tense		
Written in 1st (I) **or 3rd person** (name)		
Edit and shave Cut out unnecessary details		
Punctuation check		
Spelling and grammar check		

Editing checklist – newspaper reports

(a factual recount retelling a real event)

	✓
Interesting heading Snappy, memorable, alliterative	
Opening paragraph Answer questions Who? What? When Where? Why? Give a brief outline of the story	
Expand events in the order that they happened Use paragraphs Use time connectives: Firstly… After that… Next… Finally…	
Vivid language, powerful verbs To get an emotional reaction from the reader: 'She was *horrified* to discover…'	
Quotes eg Mrs Jones, survivor of the disaster, said " … "	
Past tense Use 'had', 'was', 'went'	
Third person Use 'he', 'she', 'they'	
Sum up eg There will be an inquiry into this catastrophe. This newspaper will keep you posted.	
Reported by (Reporter's name)	

Editing checklist – persuasive writing

(an argument from a particular point of view:
poster, leaflet, advert, letter, article)

	✔		
Catchy or alliterative phrase On advert, leaflet or poster			
Clear information Decide on your viewpoint and organize the information to support it			
Ask a question Do you want to…? Would you like it if…? Can you really…?			
Powerful language It is important to… You must realize…			
Simple psychology Everybody knows… You would be foolish not to…			
Present tense Use verbs 'is', 'are', 'have', 'can', 'like to', 'should be'			
Facts to support your point of view			
Connectives As a result of… Therefore… Consequently… etc			
Closing statement to reinforce/repeat viewpoint All the evidence shows… It's quite clear that…			
Illustration On advert, leaflet or poster			

Editing checklist – instructional writing

(an explanatory account: recipes, rules,
'how to make…', 'how to play…' etc)

	✔	
List of ingredients/equipment needed		
Ordered step-by-step approach		
Bullet points or numbers for each step		
Clear, short, simple sentences		
Imperative (or bossy) verbs to start each instruction Use present tense: Heat… Mix… Stir… etc		
Time connectives to start each instruction First… Then… Next… After that…		
Final point eg Eat and enjoy!		
Illustration(s)?		

Editing checklist – discursive writing

(an account giving different sides of a viewpoint)

	✔
Introductory statement about the topic you are discussing	
Arguments for And reasons	
Arguments against And reasons	
Paragraphs for each viewpoint	
Quotes as evidence eg: I spoke to Mr Smith, the Head Teacher, and he told me that…'	
Powerful connectives Obviously… Nevertheless… Therefore…	
Summary Sum up the discussion and give your point of view	

Editing checklist – non-chronological report writing

(a factual recount written in any order – after the introduction – about an animal, country, person or historical event)

	✔
Information Gathered mainly from books or the Internet	
Planned and clearly organized	
General introduction and opening statement	
Headings and paragraphs	
Present tense Use verbs 'is', 'are', 'have', 'can', 'like to', 'should be'	
Factual sentences	
Technical vocabulary To do with the subject matter	
Precise descriptive vocabulary eg Hamsters are inquisitive active pets.	
Pictures/fun features eg dog facts written in a paw	

It's Fun to Write

Tip Sheets

Contents

Planning and organizing story writing

Introduction

Set the scene and mood. Make it interesting so the reader wants to read on. There are five main ways to start a story:

- ❖ Description of character
- ❖ Description of setting
- ❖ A question
- ❖ Speech
- ❖ A statement

Middle section

Use the story mountain format in narrative story writing. Have a sequence of events. What happens next? Then? After that?

Climax: reach the top or high point in your story when something exciting happens.

Build up: climb up the mountain, set the scene, something starts to happen.

Resolution: climb down the mountain. What are the results of the climax?

Ending

Tie up any loose ends. It is lazy to end a story by saying 'it was all a dream'. Try using a sentence which links back to the title – a surprise or shock ending – involving the reader by saying what the character has learnt.

Do's and don'ts for planning

Don't rush into writing!

Do spend up to 10 minutes brainstorming and planning ideas.

Don't worry about writing sentences when brainstorming ideas.

Do use key words and phrases to remind you of your ideas.

Do make sure your ideas relate to the story topic.

Don't forget to arrange your ideas in logical order.

Do aim for a minimum of four paragraphs.

Do have an introduction, middle section and an ending

Expression and look	blank stare, dreamy look, glaring with anger, shame-faced, sullen, unblinking attractive, beautiful, fearsome, loathsome, repulsive, revolting, ugly
Walk	strode determinedly, sauntered cheerfully, limped painfully, marched crossly
Use adverbs to describe how the character does something	angrily, anxiously, apprehensively, bravely, calmly, carefully, carelessly, cautiously, cheerfully, clumsily, crossly, eagerly, easily, earnestly, excitedly, fearfully, furiously, gently, gladly, gratefully, greedily, grumpily, happily, hopefully, hungrily, hurriedly, impatiently, lazily, magically, mysteriously, nastily, nervously, noisily, obediently, patiently, politely, proudly, quietly, quickly, rapidly, rudely, roughly, sadly, selfishly, silently, sleepily, slowly, softly, swiftly, tearfully, thoughtfully, violently, willingly

Build up description: characters

Build	average height, chubby, lean, muscular, plump, short, slender, slim, skinny, tall
Hair	bleached blonde, dark brown, golden brown, fair haired, ginger, red, jet black, snow white, silvery grey dishevelled, frizzy, greasy, matted, tangled, thick, thinning, uncombed glossy, shiny, neatly combed bald, curly, long, pigtails, ponytail, plaits, short, wavy
Skin	clammy, freckled, lily white, lined, pale, pasty-looking, pimpled, pockmarked, scarred, suntanned, spotty, weather-beaten, wrinkled
Eyes	beady, dark brown, deep set, emerald green, sky blue, stone grey
Teeth	crooked, decaying, pearly white, protruding, razor like, rotten, sharp, yellow
Other features	birthmark, bushy eyebrows, hairy wart, long straggly beard, mole, unshaven, whiskers on chin
Hands	beautifully manicured, bitten nails, claw-like fingers, curved nails, purple veined
Voice	husky, like a foghorn, softly spoken, stuttering, wheezy, whining
Personality	(Don't forget to imply through actions) anxious, bad-tempered, boastful, cruel, cunning, finicky, foolish, fussy, greedy, grumpy, impish, irritable, lazy, long-suffering, malicious, mean, mischievous, nasty, powerful, proud, revolting, selfish, scatter-brained, silly, spiteful, vain brave, cheerful, clever, courageous, curious, eager, enthusiastic, friendly, heroic, intelligent, jolly, happy, optimistic, hard-working, warm-hearted, wise

Build up description: setting

Time of day	Light conditions
dawn	hazy rosy glow as dawn broke
early morning	sunshine streamed through the windows
lunchtime	searing blinding light
mid afternoon	dull dismal day
dusk	dimly lit... brightly lit
twilight	lengthening shadows
evening	pitch black
late evening	moonlight filtered through
midnight	stars glistened like diamonds in the moonlit sky

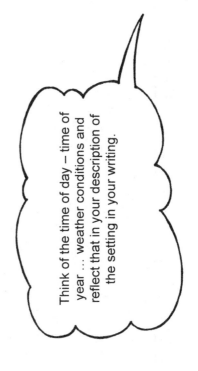

Think of the time of day – time of year ... weather conditions and reflect that in your description of the setting in your writing.

Weather

hot, cold, rainy, snowy, spring-like summery, autumnal, wintry	drizzling rain	chilly
	rain drummed rhythmically down	shrouded in damp mist
	sodden grass	autumnal leaves rustled underfoot
	dewdrops glistened in spiders' webs	dry withered leaves
	hot sunny weather	lightning zigzagged across the sky
	scented roses were entwined up the wall	torrential downpour
	water from a fountain trickled into a pool	howling wind
	waves splashed on to the warm sand	leaden grey sky
	puffy clouds	stillness ... powdery snow
	azure blue sky	frosty ground
	cloudless	white blanket of snow
	sun drenched	icicle gleamed like a glass dagger
	scorching...sweltering	bare leafless trees
	hot ... muggy	blades of grass were stiff with frost
	airless	bleak sunless landscape
	crystal clear	bitterly cold
	tranquil	wind swept
	warm starlit night	biting easterly wind

Use imagery

Use a simile

❖ Compare one thing with another, using the words 'like' and 'as'.

The leaves spun wildly on the tree like shiny discs.
The sun was like a round mirror gleaming in the sky.

Use a metaphor

❖ Describe something as if it was something else.

The mother duck was a lioness defending her chicks.
The balls of cotton wool glided across the sky.

Use personification

❖ Give a human quality to something that is not human.

Ivy twisted its fingers around the bark of the tree.
The floorboards groaned under the weight of the heavy suitcase.

Use alliteration

❖ Repeat particular sound in a series of words.

Waves of warm air wafted across my face.
The spotted snake slid slowly down the path.

Use similes, metaphors, personification, alliteration sparingly to develop description, and maximize the dramatic effect.

Build up description: setting

Short phrases to describe an old attic room

👂	...ancient floorboard creaked ...the rusty door hinge squeaked open ...rain drummed rhythmically on the roof
👁	The antique oak door at the top of the staircase had a burnished brass knob which gleamed in the dim light. Shafts of moonlight filtered through a small window in the rafter. ...a sliver of light came from behind the closed door ...the flashlight flickered and a shadowy shape danced across the wall ...old trunks full of long forgotten toys ...spotted a small black chest, slightly worse for wear, covered in a layer of dust
👃	...a musty smell of damp and mildew ...smelt an aroma of musky mothballs
✋	...felt a cold blast of air sweep over me ...a silky cobweb brushed against my face
💭	Was it my imagination, or was something moving over there? The diary had been hidden away for all those years, and I was delighted to have found it.

Involve the senses to make the reader feel part of your story and create an atmosphere. What can you see? hear? feel? smell? touch? taste?

Choose adjectives, adverbs and powerful verbs and some sensory description in your portrayal of the setting.

Involve the senses

Hear		See	
banged	murmured	attractive	glittering
bawled	popped	beautiful	gloomy
boomed	rattled	bleached	glowing
bubbled	roared	blemished	grimy
buzzed	rumbled	blurred	indistinct
cackled	rustled	bulky	marbled
chimed	scraped	burnished	mottled
chirped	screeched	carved	murky
chuckled	shattered	clean	patterned
clattered	shuffled	cluttered	polished
clicked	sizzled	crinkled	pointed
clinked	slammed	crumpled	reflective
crackled	snapped	dark	rusty
creaked	snarled	dazzling	shadowy
crunched	snored	dim	shimmering
droned	splashed	dingy	shiny
drummed	spluttered	dirty	smeared
echoed	squeaked	discoloured	smudged
fizzed	squealed	dull	sparkling
grated	squelched	faded	speckled
groaned	swished	flecked	spiralled
growled	tinkled	freckled	spotted
gurgled	twittered	fuzzy	stained
hissed	wailed	gaudy	striped
howled	whimpered	glossy	streaked
hummed	whirred	gorgeous	tarnished
jingled	whispered	gleaming	thick
lapped	whistled	glimmering	transparent
moaned	zoomed	glistening	twinkling

Feel	Smell	Touch	Taste
alarmed	aroma	bony	acidic
appreciative	aromatic	bristly	bitter
bewildered	decayed	bumpy	burnt
cheerful	festering	clammy	butterscotch
confused	fishy	cold	chocolate
excited	foul	crispy	creamy
delighted	fragrance	dry	delicious
dejected	fragranced	fluffy	insipid
embarrassed	fragrant	furry	juicy
furious	fresh	greasy	lemon
guilty	fusty	gritty	luscious
happy	musty	hairy	mouth watering
impatient	mouldy	oily	scrumptious
lonely	mildewed	prickly	sickly
nervous	odour	ridged	sour
offended	perfumed	rough	spicy
overjoyed	pungent	scaly	stale
overwhelmed	putrid	scratchy	strawberry
pleased	rank	silky	sugary
sad	reeking	slimy	sweet
satisfied	rotten	slippery	syrupy
shocked	scent	smooth	tangy
subdued	scented	spiky	tart
tearful	smell	soft	tasty
troubled	smelly	sticky	tasteless
uncertain	spicy	stubby	vanilla
uncomfortable	stale	velvety	vinegary
upset	stench	wet	watery
worried	whiff	warm	zesty

Create suspense or excitement

Use some short sentences

❖ I sat bolt upright in bed. The sound of shattering glass had woken me up.

❖ Horror struck, I froze to the spot.

❖ A cold shiver went down my spine.

❖ The fox slunk silently into the yard. He sniffed the night air. Then he crept towards the henhouse.

Ask questions

❖ She could not believe it was for her. What was in the box?

❖ Unnerved, Molly began to walk quicker. Were those footsteps behind her?

❖ Was it my imagination or did something move in the corner of the room?

Tease and keep the reader guessing

Build up the sense of expectancy by hinting rather than telling the reader straightaway what your character is going to do or the event or danger that is about to happen.

For example, on a journey to pick up a much wanted animal from the pet shop, keep hinting about the excitement to come by concentrating on the details of the car journey, the inside of the shop etc before revealing the purpose of the outing.

Use vocabulary to build up scary tension

creepy	deserted	draped in cobwebs
echoing	eerie	chilling
pale ghostly moon	pitch black	menacing
mysterious	neglected	streak of lightning
shrouded in mist	shadowy shape	sinister
spooky atmosphere	high pitched sound	the church clock chimed midnight
	reverberated	

Use a hook at the end of a paragraph

❖ The noise of the doorbell echoed through the house. Holly rushed to open the door but there was no one there. She looked to the left and to the right but the street was empty; no one was astir. Then she saw the box which had been left by the front door.

Make the mood and pace of the story vary. Have a balance of suspense, with short snappy sentences mixed with a more relaxed descriptive tone. This will serve to increase interest and heighten tension.

Remember short sentences build up suspense and longer sentences build up description.

Replace overused words with powerful verbs

said

asked	gasped	promised	stated
argued	giggled	pronounced	sniggered
bawled	groaned	questioned	taunted
begged	grumbled	remarked	teased
cackled	insisted	replied	whined
chuckled	interrupted	screamed	whispered
complained	inquired	screeched	yelled
cried	joked	scolded	wept
declared	mumbled	shouted	
demanded	murmured	sighed	
exclaimed	pleaded	sobbed	

went

ambled	hurtled	scudded	strolled
climbed	inched	scurried	tiptoed
crawled	jumped	scuttled	trudged
crept	limped	shuffled	tumbled
dashed	marched	skedaddled	wafted
drifted	plunged	slithered	walked
floated	ran	soared	wandered
flew	raced	sped	wriggled
hopped	rushed	sprinted	zoomed
hovered	sauntered	staggered	
hurried	scampered	stomped	

shone

beamed	flickered	glistened	shimmered
blazed	gleamed	glittered	smouldered
burned	glimmered	glowed	sparkled
flashed	glinted	radiated	twinkled

saw

beheld	glimpsed	perceived	spotted
detected	identified	recognized	unearthed
discovered	noticed	set eyes on	witnessed
distinguished	observed	spied	

frightened

alarmed	intimidated	scared	unnerved
appalled	panicked	startled	upset
horrified	petrified	terrified	worried

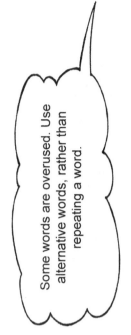

Some words are overused. Use alternative words, rather than repeating a word.

Different ways to start sentences: use connectives

One day…	Once upon a time…
A long time ago…	During the holidays…
A few months ago…	When I woke up…
Initially…	From the word go…
Just then…	At that precise moment…
Suddenly…	All of a sudden…
At once…	Immediately…
Quick as a flash…	Instantly…
In no time at all…	In the nick of time…
Unexpectedly…	Without warning…
Surprisingly…	Out of the blue…
Meanwhile…	On the other hand…
A split second later…	A moment later…
Next minute…	Before he knew it…
A little while later…	Before long…
Shortly afterwards…	As an afterthought…
After some time…	Later that day…
Eventually…	At the last minute…
Finally…	In conclusion…
When it was all over…	The following week…

Check punctuation

Capital letters
- ❖ Beginning of a sentence
- ❖ Name of a person or place
- ❖ Days of the week
- ❖ Months of the year

Commas
- ❖ Lists
  We went to the shops to get butter, sugar and eggs for the pie.
- ❖ After speech
  "I can come to the party," said Tom.
- ❖ To make sentences clear
  As a matter of fact, I'd love to.

Exclamation marks
- ❖ If something is felt strongly
  Help, I'm stuck!

Question marks
- ❖ To ask questions
  What is your name?

Apostrophes
- ❖ To make words smaller
  <u>I am</u> – <u>I'm</u> *coming to see you.*

Speech marks
- ❖ When someone is talking
  "Who is it?" whispered Amber

Story writing tips

1. Organize and plan your story
- Allow up to 10 minutes planning time.
- Write in first person (I) or third person (he/she/it).
- Make sure your writing relates to the topic throughout. Don't lose focus!

2. Remember paragraphs
- Indent each pararaph or leave a line between each.
- Paragraphs usually have 4–7 sentences.
- Paragraphs usually have one main idea.
- End each paragraph with a gripping sentence, as a hook.

3. Build up description of character and setting using interesting vocabulary
- Paint a picture with words to help the reader imagine a scene.
- Think of interesting vocabulary and powerful verbs.
- Use adjectives to make your writing more descriptive.
- Try to use similes and metaphors to make descriptions vivid.
- Use senses. What can you see? hear? smell? taste? How are you feeling?

4. Create suspense and vary sentence length to maintain reader interest
- Use long sentences for description.
- Use short sentences to give an impression of suspense, action or speed.

5. Keep in the same tense
- It is easier to write in the past tense than the present tense.

6. Use connectives
- Start your sentences in different ways to make your writing flow. Use, for example:
  Then… Suddenly… Next minute… Meanwhile… Eventually…, etc

7. Replace overused words if you need to mention something twice
- For example:
  saw – glimpsed, spied, noticed, etc

8. Use direct speech sparingly
- It can become long and boring and be difficult to punctuate.
- Start a new line when someone is speaking.

9. Take time to read over what you have written
- Check your punctuation, spelling and grammar.
- Check to see if you have left out words needed for meaning.

10. Edit and shave
- Cut out unnecessary details which don't add interest or are not needed to give meaning to the story.

Amusing animal adventure story

Title: _____

Who?
Weave the description of the animal into your story.

Ideas:
Appearance: size? look/feel of skin or fur? Special features? Walk?
Personality: timid, daring, cheeky, good natured, kindly, greedy

Setting
What does the animal see, hear, smell and feel? Use senses and simile to heighten the description. Add detail, so the readers feel they are there.

Ideas: dog in a pet shop…   horse in a stable…   mouse in hole in farmhouse…

Character
Add detail!

Ideas:
Shy dog was worried about going to a new home and having a new owner
Fat, out of condition horse wanted to lose weight and win a race
Bold mouse enjoyed going into the farmhouse and finding cheese

What happens next? Then what? After that?

Ideas:
Dog loved new home, made a friend, found something valuable when looking for bones. Who? What?
Horse found another animal to act as his personal trainer and who helped him get fit. Who? How?
Mouse got caught in a mousetrap before he could reach safety. How? Who saved him?

How is the animal feeling at the end of the story?

Boost Creative Writing, Years 5–6
© Judith Thornby and Brilliant Publications

The secret in the attic

Title: _____

Main character?

Setting

What time of day: early morning? evening? Reflect that atmosphere in your story.

Describe step-by-step the journey up to the attic: staircase, attic door, handle. What could you hear? see? smell? Use similes or personification. How were you feeling?

Ideas: floorboards creaked   well-worn steps... ivory handle shaped like... polished oak door

   strong smell of spicy cinnamon wafted   apprehensive... curious... excited...

Describe the room

Ideas: dimly lit... dusty... shaft of light flickered through... beamed roof...

What did you find?
Ideas: old diary... egg... antique pocket watch...

What is special about your find?

Ideas:
Diary belonged to a distant relative
Something unusual hatched from the egg
Watch enabled you to go back or forward in time.

What happened next? Then what? After that?

What were your thoughts about the find?

The unwelcome animal visitor in the night

Write from the point of view of a hen or mouse.

Title: _____

Set the scene
Describe the night. What can be seen? heard?
Use similes and personification to heighten description.

Ideas: distant hoot of owl… pale ghostly moon… silhouetted… shadowy shape…

In the hen house/mouse hole
Portray a cosy environment. Give the hen or mouse human characteristics.
Is there someone in the family who is a bit slow to get ready for bed, or another who is fussy, etc.

Outside the hen house/mouse hole
Add detail.
Something is moving. Contrast how the peaceful mood changes as anxiety sets in with the arrival of the unwelcome visitor – use your senses.

What could be seen of the visitor from the hen house or mouse hole?

What or who saved the hens/mice from attack?
What happened next? Then what happened? Describe in detail.

What happened to the unwelcome visitor?
Was he hurt?

What are the thoughts of the hen or mouse when the danger has passed?

Boost Creative Writing, Years 5–6
© Judith Thornby and Brilliant Publications

Adventure story

The unwelcome animal visitor in the night

Write, draw and label a mind map of ideas. Be descriptive!

What could be seen?
colours/texture/size
cluttered... tidy... squashed... roomy...

What could be heard?

What could be smelt?

What is the character feeling?

Movement/actions
powerful verbs

A spooky tale

Write a descriptive story about a man who sheltered from a storm in an old run-down house in the woods.

Title: _____

Setting – build the atmosphere
Describe the stormy weather.
Is it spring, summer, autumn or winter? Reflect the season in your description.
Use similes and personification to build up the description.
Vocabulary: lightning zigzagged across the sky.

Describe the house
Add detail.
Describe the overgrown garden, full of brambles, and the run-down house.
Bring in the senses: What could the man see? hear? smell? What was he thinking?

Ideas: derelict house… ivy twined up the walls like… broken, cracked roof tiles… dark and dingy smell… cobwebs draped…

Describe certain obstacles that the man had to deal with
Ideas: locked door … how did he get into the house?
Slippery, threadbare carpet… Did he nearly have an accident?
Sense that some ghostly presence was watching him… Why?
Loose floorboard creaked… How did he feel?

What did he find inside the house?
Ideas: old diary… scrapbook…

What were the man's thoughts when the storm was over and he could leave? Did the experience affect him?

Boost Creative Writing, Years 5–6
© Judith Thornby and Brilliant Publications

The strange encounter in the school library

Title: _____

It was the end of a busy day and all was quiet in the school. Or was it? What was happening in the school library?

Who?
Why did he/she go into the library after school? Homework task? Odd noise?
Build up the atmosphere. What was seen? heard? smelt? felt?
Use similes and personification in your descriptions.

What happened next? Add detail!
Ideas:
Open a book and pictures start to move … What book? What pictures moved?
A character from a book is in the library… Who? Why do you recognize the character?
A door appears in the wall and…

Then what happened? After that? Then? Meanwhile?

Ideas:
Character from book wants you to follow them…
You are actually in part of the story…

How did it end?
Ideas: the sound of the school bell in the distance breaks spell…
What happened to the story book character?

How did it affect the person?

The strange encounter in the school library

Read this story beginning:

> Reading isn't my strong point and I am not very keen on it. I don't find it very entertaining. In fact I think it is a waste of time. So I was not best pleased when my English teacher, Miss Penwell, told us we had to write about our favourite book as a homework task. Furthermore she expected the work to be handed in by the next day.
>
> Anyway I had a spare half hour after school, so I reluctantly decided to go to the library. There was nobody but me in the room. I was browsing through the books, idly flicking through the pages when I spotted a rather large book, at least 60 centimetres wide, hidden on a bottom shelf. It was bound in dark green leather and covered in cobwebs. There was a sickly sweet smell coming from it, like sticky toffee boiling in a pan. Of course I had to have a proper look at the book...

Discuss this writing

◆ How has the writer started the story?
  ❖ Character description
  ❖ Setting description
  ❖ Speech
  ❖ Question
  ❖ Statement
◆ How has the writer made the reader feel part of the story?
◆ Can you comment on the language used?

Boost Creative Writing, Years 5–6
© Judith Thornby and Brilliant Publications

A scary story

Opening

I was lost and alone in a solitary wasteland and night was falling like a dark blanket. It was then that I heard a low menacing howl quite nearby. I looked around and glimpsed the orange eyes of a lone wolf gleaming fiercely in the dim light. It was hungry and had caught my scent.

Without a moment's delay, I took to my heels and raced frantically towards a small coppice of trees for shelter. I knew I was in great danger as the wolf gave chase. Then I spotted the huge mansion which was half hidden in the wood, its tall towers loomed up into the dark sky. With all my energy I willed my legs to run faster and faster until I finally reached it. I pounded desperately on the door and it opened immediately, so I tore inside banging the door shut behind me.

Middle part – Who is behind the door?

Continue the story in the same style, focusing on the senses to build up descriptive tension. (Use the second sheet to help you.)

Ending

A little while later, I tumbled into the bed provided for me. All the anxiety had worn me out and I fell straight asleep. Suddenly...

Build up tension, but give a twist to the story by implying something dreadful is going to happen, when really it doesn't.

A scary story

Write the middle of the story in the same style as the opening, creating some tension.

Who is behind the door? Set the scene: How do you feel? What can you hear in the room?

Ideas:

Feelings	
scared frightened (how can you imply this?)	hands shook… heart beat widely…
Noises	
door	creaked
log fire	crackled
clock	chimed
wind	rattled
footsteps	shuffled
Who do you see? (mysterious gentleman… manservant…) What does the person look like?	
height	tall figure
walk	strode… limped…
eyes	deep set bright beady
expression/look	unblinking blank stare
skin	freckled, lily white, pale, pimpled, wrinkled, pockmarked face
hair/facial hair	ginger, jet black, snow white, silvery, greasy, matted, thinning, long haired, bushy eyebrows, straggly beard
voice (speech)	"I've been expecting you," murmured a man in a voice booming like a foghorn.

Choose any words in the grid that fit in with the character you have thought of. Add your own words, using a thesaurus if needed.

Boost Creative Writing, Years 5–6
© Judith Thornby and Brilliant Publications

The bubble that manages to break free and escape

Title: _____

"It's so lovely to be free," the bubble thought with relief.

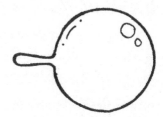

Where?
Use simile and personification in your description. What does the bubble look like? How is the bubble feeling?

Ideas: water bubble in a saucepan… air bubble in lemonade… soap bubble in bath…

Vocabulary: hot, cramped, claustrophobic, depressed, sad, restless, agitated, keyed up, translucent, lustrous, opaque, luminous, etc.

What happened next? How did it break free?
Ideas:
Grew bigger?
Thicker?
Stronger?
Changed colour?
Thought powerful thoughts?

Then what happened? After that? Then? Meanwhile?

Ideas: into the garden… high up into the sky… over the sea… to a different country…

Vocabulary: floated, skimmed across, gradually gained momentum

What happened next? After that? Then?
What did the bubble see? hear? smell? touch?
How was it feeling as it went on its journey?

Did it end happily for the bubble or not?

This page may be photocopied for use by the purchasing institution only.

First person fantasy story

What happened when you bought an unusual present from a shop?

Title: _____

Interesting starting sentence

Where was the shop? How did it look from the outside?
Did you find the shop by accident? Were you looking for it?
Make the reader feel involved. Describe the setting in detail.

Ideas: down a deserted side street… on the outskirts of town… in a busy airport…

What sort of shop was it inside? Add detail!
Ideas: antique shop… toy shop… sports shop… gift shop…

What things caught your eye? What did you buy?
Anything unusual about it – strangely light/heavy… odd colour, etc.

What about the sales assistant?
Did he/she remind you of anyone? – Merlin-type or fairy godmother type character, etc.
Did he/she warn you about your purchase?

What happened next? Was it a present for you or for someone else?

What happened next that caused a bit of trouble?
Ideas: during the day… the following day…

Was the trouble resolved? What were your feelings about it all?

Boost Creative Writing, Years 5–6
© Judith Thornby and Brilliant Publications

A descriptive account of a beach

Heighten your description with the use of similes, metaphors and personification. Bring in the senses and use interesting verbs.

Title: _____

What can you see?

Ideas: sun, sand, sea, waves, clouds, palm trees, rock pools, cliffs, boats, fish, crabs, shells, seaweed, coral, rocks, lighthouse, grassy dunes, lights

What can you hear?

Ideas: children, waves, seagulls, surf, wind

What can you smell?

Ideas: salty spray, ozone, sun tan oil, decaying seaweed

What can you taste?

Ideas: perspiration, food from vendor?

How do you feel?

Ideas: relaxed, happy, soothed, calm, refreshed, peaceful

A descriptive account of a beach

Read this descriptive account:

It was quieter on the beach now and the light had dimmed as the sun slowly set. The evening breeze tickled my skin and ruffled my long hair playfully as I sat on the cold stone wall. The palm trees behind me stood still and watchful.

I listened to the rhythmic lapping of the waves as the water ebbed and flowed over the soft damp sand. The sea seemed more at peace now compared to the angry heave and swell of surf earlier in the day.

I watched the solid shape of a huge liner etched against the horizon move steadily onwards. I stayed put for a short while until the moon gently painted the water with silvery light, and the stars, like tiny diamonds, started to twinkle in the night sky.

I was roused from my reverie by the delicious aroma of tapas coming from a familiar restaurant on the other side of the road. I inhaled the salty tang of the sea and breathed a silent sigh of contentment as I made my way quickly to my workplace again. I felt refreshed and invigorated by the brief period of time that I had spent on the beach.

Discuss this writing

◆ What time of day is it? How do you know?

◆ How has the writer made the reader involved?

◆ What descriptive devices have been used?

Boost Creative Writing, Years 5–6
© Judith Thornby and Brilliant Publications

A day in your life which you remember well

Title: _____

Interesting starting sentence

Idea: I remember the day clearly because of what happened. It all started…

Build up the atmosphere of excitement
Don't give too much away at this stage. Make the reader feel involved. What do you remember seeing? hearing? tasting? smelling? How were you feeling?

When?
Ideas: a school day… weekday… weekend…

Where are you at first?
Ideas: at home getting ready to… at the hospital waiting… in a car going to…

What was about to happen that would made the day memorable?

Ideas:
starting a new school
moving into a new house
having a special birthday treat

seeing a baby brother or sister for the first time
collecting a new puppy, kitten or other pet

What happened at first?
Describe in detail, step-by-step.

Then what happened? After that?

What are your feelings now about that day?

Rescue from the Titanic

Set the scene
Who? (man/woman/child/rich/poor)

Where were you on the boat on the night the Titanic hit the iceberg?

What did you do when you realized the Titanic was sinking?
Describe order of events in the right order, step-by-step.
How did you get to the top deck?
Did you get into a lifeboat?
What could you see? hear? smell? How were you feeling?

How did you escape? What are your lasting memories?

Vocabulary

shuddered	rammed	iceberg	top deck
jostled	fight for survival	eerie	perpendicular
musicians played on	terrified	bitterly cold	fingers numb
swamped by waves	horror	darkest hour before dawn	

Read quotes from survivors and weave them into your story.

Boost Creative Writing, Years 5–6
© Judith Thornby and Brilliant Publications

Rescue from the Titanic

Beginning

Who? Where were you on the boat?
Opening lines need to interest the reader.

Middle

What did you do when you realized the Titanic was sinking?
Remember the different senses: sounds, sights, smells, tastes, touch.
What were you feeling? Use dramatic words: imagery, simile, metaphor.

Conclusion

How did you escape? What are your lasting memories?

Dear Diary

What did Theseus write in his diary the day he killed the Minotaur?

Opening sentence

Dear Diary,
You won't believe the day I've had today…

What was it like in the labyrinth?

What could you hear?

What could you see?

What could you smell?

How were you feeling

What was the Minotaur like? How did you kill it?
What did the Minotaur look like? What did he smell like? How were you feeling?

Vocabulary:

half man half bull	hideous	strong	frightful red eyes
glared	bellowed	worried	fierce battle
Instantly…	After a while…	Quick as a flash…	Finally…

How did you find your way out of the labyrinth?
Are you glad? Why?

Vocabulary: magic thread… Ariadne, daughter of King Minos

Closing sentence
Idea: Anyway, I can't wait to tell father I've killed the Minotaur…

Boost Creative Writing, Years 5–6
© Judith Thornby and Brilliant Publications

My newspaper report

Pick a well-known story and write your version as a newspaper report. Give your version a twist!

Headline
(Make it catchy)

Write down your facts in the correct order
Pick one story. Answer the questions:

When?

Who?

Where was the person?

What was the person doing?

Why was he/she doing it?

What happened?

Questions for reporter to ask?

Idea (to ask the wolf in The Three Little Pigs): Why did you blow the pigs' house down?

Add quotes
(What people involved in the story said)

Ideas:
"I am disgusted that the children..." the witch told me.
"Humpty knows that he should not..." said his mother.

My newspaper report

Reporter:

Boost Creative Writing, Years 5–6
© Judith Thornby and Brilliant Publications

A day in the sweatshop – plan for report

What are sweatshops?

Sweatshops, or sweat factories as they are sometimes called, are places where people are employed to make goods cheaply and where they are treated badly.

Pay

poorly paid
children expected
  to do adult jobs
less than minimum
  wage

Sweatshops

Working hours/hazards

long 12-hour day
tiredness causing accidents
few breaks
fingers trapped in machines
no proper training
hardly any days off

Types of jobs

using sewing machines
stitching
mixing chemicals

Factory conditions

filthy… cramped
lots of people sleeping in
  factory
unhygienic
eyes irritated by chemicals
  in dyes and fibres
little proper nourishment

Write a diary entry about a day working in a sweatshop.

Use and expand the ideas in the plan.

A day in the sweatshop
– a diary entry

Tuesday evening

I woke up this morning and just could not face another hard day's work at the factory. I know that I have to do the work because it is so difficult to get a job and somebody else will just take my place...

Boost Creative Writing, Years 5–6
© Judith Thornby and Brilliant Publications

What snacks should be allowed in school?

Should the only snacks allowed at school be fruit? Discuss and give your point of view.

Introduce argument
Ideas: There is an argument for and against promoting fruit and banning sweets, cakes and chocolate as snacks in school.

Reasons for? Add detail

Ideas:
Increase brain power
More tasty
Feel good factor

Full of glucose which gives energy
Look forward to…

Reasons against? Add detail

Ideas:
Unhealthy/better for you
Cause allergic reaction
Causes litter

Rot your teeth
Could spoil appetite

Quote(s) supporting the case for or against

Idea: *I spoke to _____ who told me…*

Head teacher   Pupil   Caretaker   Canteen manager

Sum up and give your point of view

Ideas:
Obviously…
Nevertheless…
Therefore…

Persuasive

Persuasive article for the Nursery Rhyme Gazette

Title:
Should _____

Reported by: _____

Opening
The *Nursery Rhyme Gazette* newspaper carefully presents both sides of an argument. This week we are discussing whether:

Ideas:
Should Wolf be blamed for scaring Little Red Riding Hood?
Should Goldilocks be charged for breaking into the Bear family home?
Should Mrs Dumpty be blamed for being a poor mother?

Reasons for? Add detail	**Reasons against? Add detail**

Quote(s) supporting the case for or against

Ideas:
I spoke to…
He/she said…

Sum up and give your point of view
Having given this matter with some thought…

Useful words for discussion

First of all	On the other hand	Some people would consider
It could be argued that	Many people believe	Those who think this argue
Furthermore they suggest	In addition they think	Some would argue
Finally they think	Furthermore	Obviously
In conclusion	Nevertheless	This newspaper believes
In my opinion	Therefore	Consequently

Boost Creative Writing, Years 5–6
© Judith Thornby and Brilliant Publications

Write and design a persuasive poster

Be an eco-friendly school!

Slogan

Layout
Plan to use all the sheet!

Illustration
Size? Detail? Colour? Position?

Facts
Make points clear.

Persuasive language

Ideas:
It is important to…
Why not…
Help by…
Think about?

Vocabulary

energy	waste	recycle	bins	paper use
double sided	switch off	stand by	close	use less
water	water butts	nature garden	pond wildlife	vegetables
compost	wormery	travel	walk	cycle
share a car	little	responsibility	improve environment	

A mystery story – whodunnit?

The mystery
Ideas:

The mystery of the stolen cupcakes	The mystery of the missing blue paint	The mystery of the missing white furry kittens

The setting
Describe in detail what can be seen, heard or smelt.
Ideas:

Cook's kitchen: … busily mixing… delicious aroma of… smell wafted out of the window… at last ready to decorate…	School caretaker's storeroom: shelves full of… everything tidily stacked away, Mr .... fussily sorting out…	Cat breeder's house: strong whiff of fish, red carpet covered in silky white cat hairs, busy vacuuming… did not hear the front door open and someone creep in…

The characters

Ideas:

Detective   Cook/caretaker/cat breeder   Suspect   Red herring

Special characteristics
Ideas:

scratches ear to think	drives a red sports car
eats a lot of sweets	very short sighted, wore thick rimmed spectacles
extra large feet	bright red hair
nervous twitch… worried expression… guilty look	

The clues

Ideas:

cake crumbs leading to…	big footprints belonging to a large man in the soil
blue paint on finger	red hair left at scene
sweet wrapper left at crime scene	white kitten fluff on suspect's jumper
Mr/Mrs .... was seen leaving the scene of the crime	

Whodunnit? The motive
Ideas:

Wanted to win the cake competition and was jealous of the beautiful cakes made by…	Took the paint because he/she had no money to finish off painting…	Wanted to make snow shoes out of kittens' fur because he/she was an evil person

Boost Creative Writing, Years 5–6
© Judith Thornby and Brilliant Publications

Whodunnit – structure

Setting of the mystery	Set the scene. Make the reader feel as if he/she was there. What could be seen? heard? smelt?		
Introduce characters	Main character(s)	Suspect	Red herring
	Write a paragraph about each character. Add detail so the reader gets a good picture of what they look like and how they behave. What was each character thinking? Suggest that they might be the culprit and have taken something, even if they have not.		
The discovery	Something has gone missing. When or how was it discovered that something had disappeared?		
The detective is on the trail	**Either** Be the detective and work out who was the culprit, weaving it into the story. What clues led you to solve the mystery? What put you off the trail? What was the reason why it happened? What were your thoughts about it? **Or** Fill in a detective report. Who were the suspects? What were the clues? Who was the culprit? What was the motive?		
Clues			
Whodunnit?			
Motive			
Final thoughts			

Whodunnit – report by detective

What was the mystery?

Where did it take place?

Evidence/clues	Left by

Whodunnit?	Reason why?

Boost Creative Writing, Years 5–6
© Judith Thornby and Brilliant Publications

Whodunnits – vocabulary used

Mystery story

detective	investigator or person who tries to solve a mystery
sidekick	assistant, helper
culprit	person who has committed a wrong doing
suspect	person detective thinks might have done something wrong
red herring	something or someone that puts detective off the trail
evidence	anything that proves someone has committed a crime
clues	signs of evidence
witness	an onlooker, observer
alibi	a good reason why a person could not have done something wrong
innocent	harmless, not guilty
guilty	has done something wrong, broken the law
motive	the reason why
interview	ask someone questions to find out what they think or know
confess	own up, come clean

Mystery story

The case of the missing prize pumpkin

It all started one chilly day last September. The famous detective Sam Gumshoe was relaxing in his penthouse flat in Baker Street stroking his dog Basil, a rather clever West Highland Terrier, when the phone rang. It was a Mr Trowel who was a member of the local gardening group in Gerrards Cross. He sounded almost tearful and wanted Sam Gumshoe's urgent help.

Having nothing better to do, Sam decided to pay Mr Trowel a visit. Donning his blue checked blazer which he always wore, whether the weather was hot or cold, he whistled to Basil and they cheerfully rushed down the stairs to the smart red sports car which was parked just outside the flat. They drove down the A40 in record time and arrived about half an hour later at Mr Trowel's house. Sam knocked on the door and it was opened by a young woman who told him she was Mr Trowel's housekeeper, Rosie Thomas. She led him and Basil out into the garden but seemed a little nervous as she introduced Sam to her employer.

Mr Trowel was a small man with a bald head who was about 50 years of age. He was standing by his greenhouse looking extremely cross. He told Sam that he had gone down to his greenhouse that morning and found that his prize pumpkin had disappeared, so that he could not enter it in the big competition that was being held the next day. Sam could barely hear what he was saying as loud pop music was blaring forth from the house at the bottom of his garden.

"I'll report her to the police again," he said angrily, " Gilly Gas is always playing her music too loudly."

Then he left Sam and Basil to look around the garden for clues. The detective saw it was beautifully kept; the lawn was neatly trimmed and there was a huge flower bed crammed with shrubs and colourful flowers and a vegetable plot at the bottom of the garden.

Sam spotted Mr Trowel's neighbour, a tall man staring at him over the fence, but when he went and leaned over the fence to talk there was no sign of him. He noted that the tall man also had a big vegetable patch in his garden. However he was distracted by the sound of Basil barking. When he went to see what the matter was he saw Basil had found some very large footprints in the soil that led to the gate at the bottom of the garden.

Discuss this writing

◆ Can you spot any likely suspects?

◆ Why do you think they might be suspects?

◆ What might be the reason each of them might have for taking the pumpkin?

Boost Creative Writing, Years 5–6
© Judith Thornby and Brilliant Publications

Poem about a rainforest animal or plant

Use imagery – simile, metaphor, personification.

Choose one catchy repeating line:

Ideas:
Deep in the rainforest
Hidden in the rainforest

Animal? Tree? Plant?
Look at pictures!

Ideas: orang-utan, red-eyed tree frog, toucan, anaconda, tarantula, nibung palm tree

Simile	Compares one thing with something else using the words 'like' or 'as' *… with skin as cold as ice* *… with a beak like polished gold*
Metaphor	Compares two different things but states that something is something else *… with **white daggers** for **teeth***
Personification	Gives a human quality to something that is not human *… clinging to a lush green stem which **groans** under its weight*

Example:

Deep down in the rainforest
There is an eyelash viper
Long limbless elastic skin
Brightly coloured as yellow mustard
Inching slowly down a leaf
Like a ferocious warrior

Deep down in the rainforest…

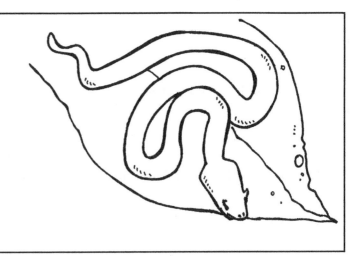

Poem about a rainforest animal or plant

Use imagery – simile, metaphor, personification.

Choose a striking part of an animal/plant/tree
Vividly compare it with something else.

fur	glowing like amber
teeth	gleaming like frosted icicles
/	

Ideas: eyes, teeth, fur, beak, skin, bark

Movement – how?

Size – as small as…, as tall as…

Boost Creative Writing, Years 5–6
© Judith Thornby and Brilliant Publications

Poem about a rainforest animal or plant

Use imagery – simile, metaphor, personification.

_____
_____(repeating line)

There is a_____

_____

_____

_____

_____

_____
_____(repeating line)

There is a_____

_____

_____

_____

A simile poem

Similes compare one thing to another using the words 'like' or 'as'. They add description to your creative writing.

1. Visualize a picture of a pet animal, family member or yourself to describe.
2. Decide on five components that you will use and create similes to describe them.

Draft your similes on the sheet below. Have fun experimenting with them! Pick the ones you like best. (Don't forget to include some adjectives.)

Components	Ideas	Ideas
hair	Your hair is as… His hair is as… Her hair is as… My hair is as…	soft, silky, curly, spiky, brown velvet cushion, coiled spring, autumn leaf
eyes	Your eyes are like… His eyes are as Her eyes twinkle like… My eyes are as…	
ears		
legs/tail		
body		
teeth/lips		
fingers/claws		
brain		
voice/bark/purr		
smile/character trait (busy, happy, etc)		

Boost Creative Writing, Years 5–6
 © Judith Thornby and Brilliant Publications

A simile poem

_____

_____

_____

_____

_____

_____

_____

_____

By _____

Who is your poem about?

brother, dad, sister, friend, cousin, pet, me

Recurring line?

He…, She…, You…, Sister…, Me…, etc

Example:

She
Her body is as thin as a rake
She
Her hair is as curly as the rippling waves

Play script

The Battle of Hastings 1066
(a play script)

Use this information to create your play.

Cause of battle

In 1066 Edward the Confessor (Anglo-Saxon king of England) died. He had no children so Harold, the head of the most powerful noble family in England, was crowned king.

Other people wanted the throne. Edward the Confessor's cousin William, Duke of Normandy, and the King of Norway were the main challengers.

The first challenge was from the King of Norway who Harold defeated at Stamford Bridge. Then almost straight after he had to march 200 miles to Hastings to face William and his Norman army who had just arrived fresh from France .

Let battle commence…..!

BATTLE OF HASTINGS – 14th October 1066

Early morning
9.00 am Harold and his army took up position at the top of a hill near Hastings and the battle with William and the Norman army began.

Midday
Normans kept charging up the hill but the English army stood strong with their shields raised. Fierce fighting but the Normans could not break through and the English army seemed to be winning.

Early afternoon
Normans tricked Saxons by pretending to retreat. Harold made a fatal mistake by ordering his army to go down the hill and chase the Normans. William ordered his army to turn round and fight. All out attack – many Saxons are hacked down.

A bit later
William ordered his archers to strike. King Harold shot in the eye and killed. Saxon army falls to pieces.

William the Conqueror will now be the first Norman king of England

Think of your cast and the stage instructions and scenes.

Ideas for the cast:

Cast
Harold – King of Saxon England
William – Norman invader
Norman soldier on horse
Norman archer
Saxon foot soldier
Saxon peasant

Boost Creative Writing, Years 5–6
© Judith Thornby and Brilliant Publications

The Battle of Hastings 1066 (a play script)

Cast:

Stage instruction(s):

Speaker	What they say

Conversations overheard

Conversations in the classroom

"Please Miss," I begged.

" No," she shouted.

"I feel ill Miss, can I go home?" I asked.

"Stop making a fuss Holly," she
spluttered and her face went red with
fury as she spoke.

"Can you hear them?" whispered Eliza
to Sylvie.

"Nobody displeases Miss Spittlemouth,"
replied Sylvie.

"Holly does look a bit green, I hope she
isn't sick again," mumbled Eliza.

 "Have you done your history homework?" hissed Cathy from the
other side of the room.

 "Oh my gosh, I didn't do it – don't tell Mr Thomas," exclaimed
Bella.

"The boys are going nuts next door, I am going to need help with
this," begged Miss Cattelworth as she stormed into the classroom.

"I will deal with you later Holly," roared Miss Spittlemouth as she
stomped out of the room.

"That will be nice," I thought sarcastically.

Boost Creative Writing, Years 5–6
© Judith Thornby and Brilliant Publications

Conversations overheard

Play script

Write a mini-story in the form of a play script that can be acted out

---

Use different words for 'says' to inform the stage instructions

Ideas:

questions	laughs	groans	grasps	argues
whispers	cries	yells	sighs	grumbles
explains	chuckles	jokes	whinges	murmurs
asks	mutters	remarks	screams	criticizes

Where?	**Cast**
Ideas:	Names of people involved (3–4)
In the classroom	
On a coach	
Round the breakfast table	

Idea: **The surprise letter**
Scene 1

Cast:
Lucy
Mum
Poppy
Joe

(Lucy, Mum, Poppy and Joe are all having breakfast in the kitchen)

Mum:　　　　Is that a knock on the door?

Lucy:　　　　I'll go, I'm expecting some post. *(Shouts as she hurries to the door)*

Lucy:　　　　I don't believe it! *(Whispers as she sits down again at the table)*

Poppy:　　　What's the matter? *(Mumbles while eating her cornflakes)*

Lucy:　　　　I'm one of the winners of a short story competition organized by Radio 2. *(gasps excitedly)*

Poppy:　　　You dark horse. I didn't know that you had the time for writing – you are always at the gym.

Lucy:　　　　Miss Jones encouraged us to send a story in the other week.

Mum:　　　　What's that you just said Lucy?

Joe:　　　　Apparently, Lucy has won a writing competition. *(Sighs Joe in a bored manner as he gets up from the table)*

Mum:　　　　Well I think that is amazing, clever girl! *(Remarks, clapping her hands)*

William Shakespeare – my autobiography

Facts about me
Place of birth
Birth – death
Details about my family
Marriage
Where I lived?

My career
Where did I start my acting career?
What did I write? How many?

Vocabulary:

| actor | playwright | plays | histories | comedies | tragedies | sonnets |

My most popular plays

Famous lines I wrote (quotes)

Important events affecting the performance of my plays

1559	Elizabeth I proclaimed travelling players could have own permanent indoor theatres
1576	James Burbidge built first theatre called The Theatre
1596	Black Death or plague rife and caused death of my son Hamnet
1597	Lease of The Theatre ran out so it was demolished. Wood from it was used to build Globe
1599	Globe theatre built
1613	Globe theatre burnt down
1614	New Globe theatre built (on same site as present-day Globe theatre)
1642	Reign of Cromwell – Puritans closed down the theatres
1660	Charles II reopened theatres/playhouses

Boost Creative Writing, Years 5–6
© Judith Thornby and Brilliant Publications

William Shakespeare – my autobiography

Shakespeare

Introduction

My autobiography

Globe theatre

Facts about me

The theatre/ playhouse

My plays

Why was it so popular?

Who were the actors?

Where were my plays performed?

Quotes

Lord Chamberlain's Men
theatre company – Shakespeare part owner

What happened when the Puritans shut down the theatres?

People who came to the theatre

The Gallants
Upper class - finest clothes – wanted to be seen – posies attached to wrists to take away smell

Cutpurses
No pockets in clothes – cut purses from belts of rich – prime place to steal

Penny stinkards
Pay penny – stand in front of stage – poor – no money for soap – smelt

Don't forget to make it interesting!
Snappy introduction
Headings
Pictures and diagrams (label different bits)
Fun features: facts in thought bubbles, etc.

Macbeth

Write a descriptive account as if you were an observer of an encounter between three witches and two soldiers, based on the opening scenes of Macbeth.

Setting: description of the moor
Build up an atmosphere of foreboding (no characters at this stage)
What can be heard? seen? smelt?

Characters. Focus on detail (no speech yet)

Witches	Soldiers
Ideas: Visual experience What are they doing? Power Pets (familiar animal spirits)	Two distant figures could be spotted crossing the moor. As they got closer it was obvious that they were… Ideas: Describe how the soldiers looked – unwashed, bloodied battle dress, etc How would they be walking and behaving after winning a long weary battle?

On first sighting the witches, how do the soldiers react?

What spells are the witches mumbling?
Make up a spell – add ingredients (eye of newt, etc).

Hubble, bubble toil and trouble
Fire burn and cauldron bubble

_____

_____

Macbeth

Write a descriptive account of the moor, inspired by the opening scenes of Macbeth. Build up an atmosphere of foreboding!

Setting: what could be seen on the moor?

Setting: what could be heard on the moor?

Setting: what could be smelt on the moor?

Vocabulary and useful phrases

depressing – gloomy – lonely – eerie – bleak – sinister – dark – cold – damp – foggy – grey – leaden – shadows – jagged rocks – overgrown with nettles – barren wasteland – signs of a recent battle in bloodied marsh water – thunder clap – wind howled – moaned – wailed – stink – rotting – foul – putrid – decayed

---

Macbeth

Write a descriptive account of the three witches, inspired by the opening scenes of Macbeth.

Witch 1	
Power	
Appearance	
Pet (familiar) name – other detail	

Witch 2	
Power	
Appearance	
Pet (familiar) name – other detail	

Witch 3	
Power	
Appearance	
Pet (familiar) name – other detail	

Ideas:

Think of the witches as women, but focus on particular weird details of their appearance. Remember: their strangeness made a brave soldier like Macbeth feel uneasy.

… charcoal grey face with one normal eye and one fiery yellow snake eye…

Vocabulary and useful phrases

snake – raven – crow – bewitch the mind – guard of – massive volcano erupts when she shouts – hideous – repulsive – bearded mole

Boost Creative Writing, Years 5–6
© Judith Thornby and Brilliant Publications

Midsummer Night's Dream

Shakespeare

Write a descriptive account of Midsummer Night's Eve.

Somebody is astir – a very special feast is about to start. In fact, anything can happen; it is almost like a Midsummer Night's dream…

Opening sentence

It is Midsummer Night's Eve, the most magical night in the year…

Set the scene: where? who is first about? (humans are all asleep)

Use similes and bring in the senses. What can be heard, seen and smelt?

Ideas:

By a giant toadstool at the bottom of the garden   Deep in the woods
On top of a grassy hill   In amongst the mayflowers

Vocabulary:
tiptoed – fluttered – excitement – commotion

Preparations for the party

Ideas: decorations – lighting – food – music

Arrival of the guests

What do they look like? What are they wearing?

Ideas:
Mischievous elves – pixies – gnomes
Beautiful fairies with delicate wings like…
Tiny leprechaun – will o' the wisp
Majestic unicorn with a silver horn that glistened like…
Exquisite butterflies

Main event

Ideas: start of the dancing – arrival of the Fairy Queen – the Queen's speech

---

End of the party – reflecting on events

Maybe something is left and is found by a child in the morning…

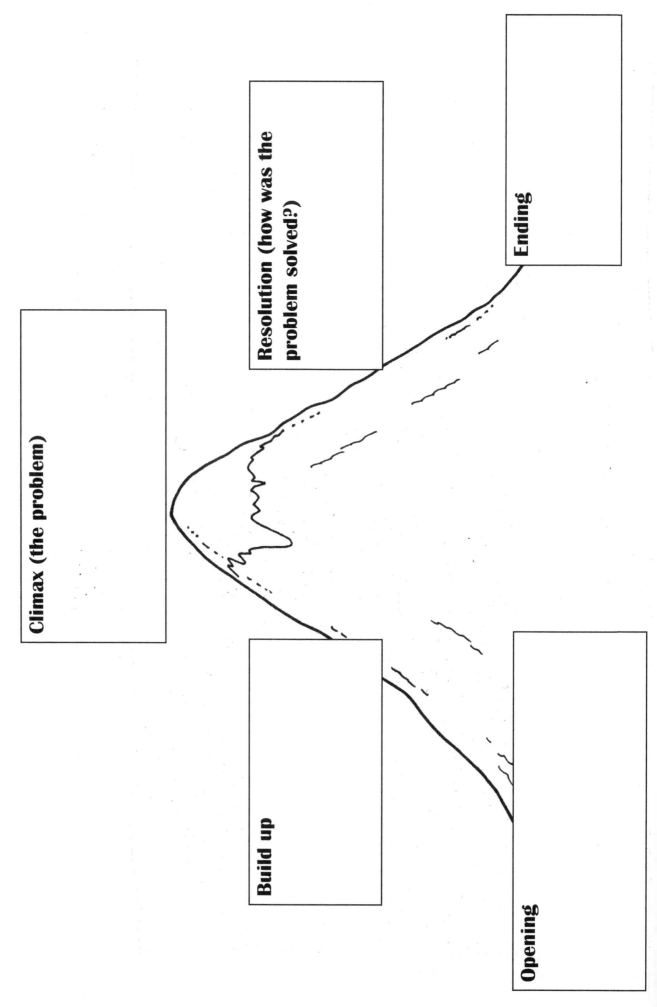

Resolution (how was the problem solved?)

Ending

Climax (the problem)

Build up

Opening

Boost Creative Writing, Years 5–6
© Judith Thornby and Brilliant Publications

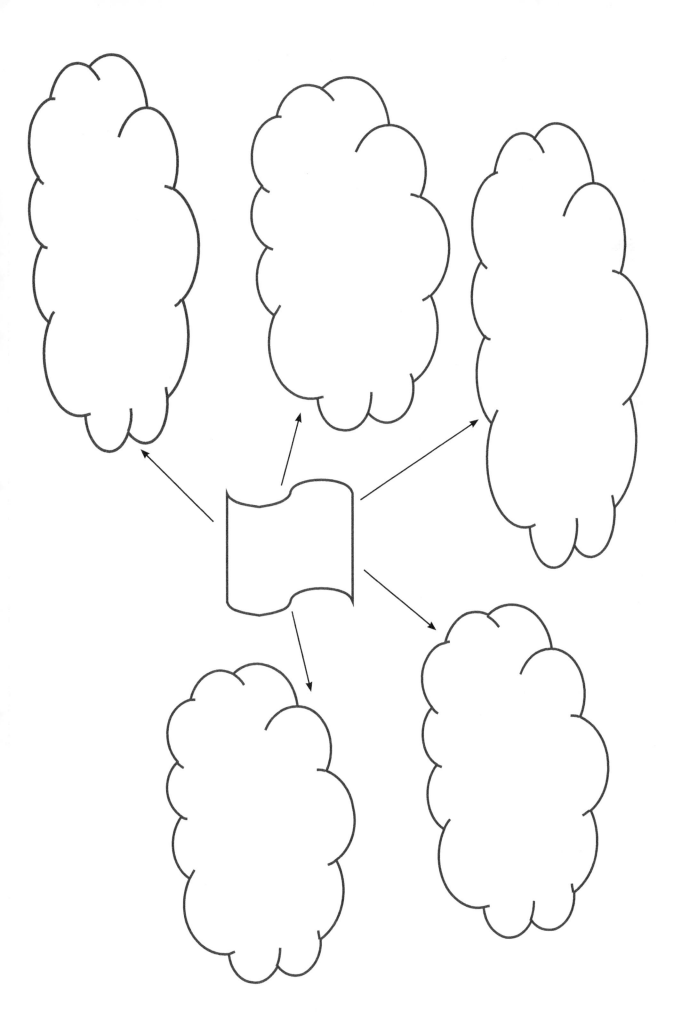

Bring in the senses

Use this sheet to use your senses when you plan your descriptive story.

Title: _____

Boost Creative Writing, Years 5–6